High-Frequency READERS™

W9-BAX-656

IN THE Forest

Written by Melissa Schiller
Illustrated by Margaret Kasahara

Scholastic Inc.
New York   Toronto   London   Auckland   Sydney
Mexico City   New Delhi   Hong Kong

No part of this publication may be reproduced in whole or in part, or stored in a retrieval system, or transmitted in any form or by any means, electronic, mechanical, photocopying, recording, or otherwise, without written permission of the publisher. For information regarding permission, write to: Permissions Department, Scholastic Inc., 555 Broadway, New York, NY 10012.

ISBN 0-439-17365-5

12 11 10 9   10 11 12/0
Printed in the U.S.A.   23
First Scholastic clubs printing, January 2000

What do you see?
I see a tree.

What do you see?
I see a deer drinking water.

What do you see?
I see a rabbit in the grass.

What do you see?
I see a bear eating berries.

What do you see?
I see an owl sleeping in a tree.

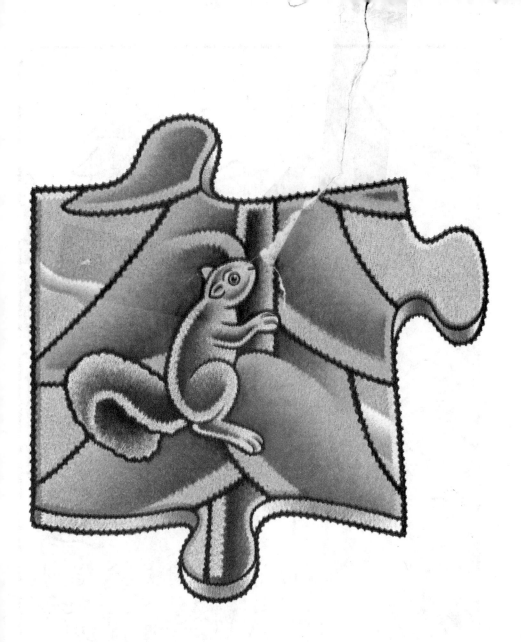

What do you see?
I see a squirrel climbing up a tree.

I see the forest.
What do you see?